The National Elf Service
not the
NHS

First published in the UK 2016, 2nd edition 2016

ISBN   9781854570895

Published by: Clinical Press Ltd., Redland Green Farm, Redland, Bristol, BS6 7HF, UK.

www.clinicalpress.co.uk

The National Elf Service

not the
NHS

A tragi-comedy in several parts
portrayed in cartoon form
by
Paul R Goddard

Dedicated to the memory of my many friends who died too young whilst working for the NHS.

Introduction

This project started when a colleague asked me to talk to BAPIO* about the loss of the art of medicine...the declining of clinical skills of history taking and examination.
I agreed to give the talk but decided to illustrate the message using cartoons penned by myself.... cartoons about the National Elf Service and not the NHS!
And here they are...I hope that they both amuse and inform.
Please enjoy them and feel free to contact me to make suggestions for future cartoons.

Kind regards

Paul R Goddard
BSc, MBBS, MD, DMRD, FRCR, FBIR, FHEA

* the British Association of Physicians of Indian Origin

Getting started

When asked to give the talk (entitled The Losing Art of Clinical Medicine and how can we restore it?) my initial thought was that we might be wrong.

Perhaps we were not really losing the skills but were simply becoming grouchy old men as epitomised in the cartoon above?

Mentors

......Then I remembered my mentors...great men and women from the past who had taught me the art of medicine.

Heroes of the Golden Age of the National Elf Service (not the NHS). A time when our health service was widely acknowledged as the very best in all the World.

Lesson number one from the Professor of Medicine is shown above and number two is opposite........

'If they are ill give them a pill'

No! ....Not 'If they are ill give them a pill'.
This appocryphal message of the physicians was never espoused by our mentors! From each patient we had to take a full and detailed history and careful examination and they were adamant that it was essential we had clinical freedom to treat patients to the best of our ability and for the patients' greatest good.

4

But how did that fit in with the new regime ? How can you take a history if you will only allow one ailment to be discussed?

And what has become of Clinical Freedom when the managers, with no medical training, decide on which drugs can be prescribed and which surgeon the patient can see?

'If in doubt cut it out'

My mind wandered to the spurious surgical motto 'If in doubt cut it out'.

Now that there are league tables of surgical performance many surgeons are becoming choosy about whom they will operate upon. In some ways this may be a good thing but if surgery is the only chance for a patient and the surgeons will not operate......

The Surgical Super-Star

The Surgical Super-Star, hero of the past as pictured above, was also a great mentor. He undoubtedly worked himself too hard in heroic manner. His motto was that of the great Hippocrates...**first do no harm**. But he would always operate if it gave the patient a fighting chance.

He is sorely missed

8

So maybe my colleague, Professor Gandhi, was right... perhaps the Art of Clinical Medicine was in danger of being lost.
To back this thesis my colleague had sent the following email:

Read the following post on social media.
Have not checked all facts yet, but if true, then very worrying.

584 doctors erased in 133 years from 1858 to 1991 (BMJ, RWakefield) Average 4 per year
Approximately an average off 50 doctors a year are erased in recent years
Are Standards of doctors in UK falling ?

So are we really losing the art of clinical medicine?
And if so, why?

The realisation dawned.
I was being asked to talk about **Clinical Standards** with a capital **C** and a capital **S**

A contentious subject. Best illustrated by my own cartoons of totally imaginary people in the National Elf Service. Any similarity with person or persons living or dead thus being entirely coincidental.

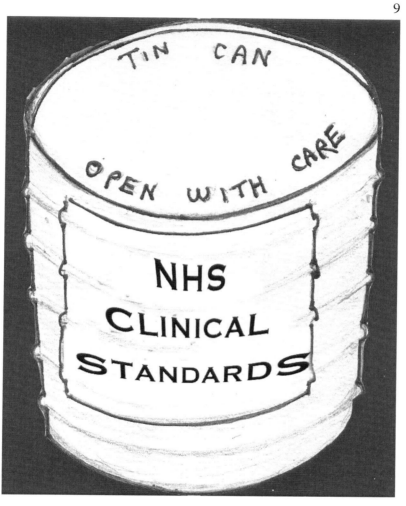

Should I open the can?

It was bound to be a can of worms!

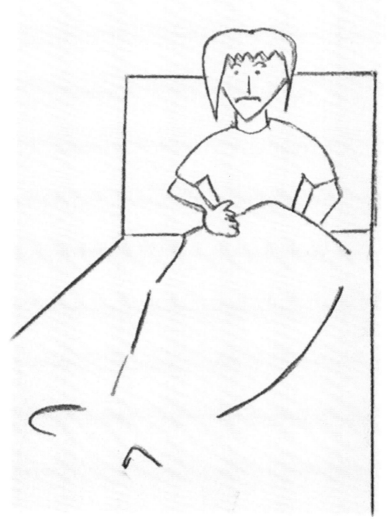

Mrs. Peabody

And here is the first of my imaginary patients in the National Elf Service of Elfdom in Farie. Mrs. Peabody presented with backache and weight gain.

Mr. Molesworth

And the second is poor Mr. Molesworth. He is a pixie who has a Colles' Fracture. More about him later but first we will learn what happened to Mrs. Peabody.......

13

The doctors in today's National Elf Service 'order' many more investigations than they used to in the past. This might be OK if they have properly examined the patient and taken a decent history but if they haven't they may well be led in the wrong direction.........

14

Oh dear...

The doctor has gone straight for investigations and referrals. Let us hope it works out OK...

Already going slightly wrong. The referrals to the podiatrist and chiropracter are not going to happen even though the podiatrist is available in the hospital. The same would occur if the referral had been made to another consultant such as a surgeon or diabetologist. It does seem rather crazy.

What about all the investigations?

The Sword of Damocles hangs over the GP as she tells Mrs. Peabody the bad news that none of the results from the investigations have reached the surgery computer. But still Mrs. Peabody has not had a proper history taken or a thorough physical examination.

It may not be the fault of the GP surgery. Perhaps the investigations have not been done yet?
Maybe they are 'on the pile' rather than on the official waiting list?

Does this really happen? ....You can bet your bottom dollar it does!

The Pile

The Waiting List

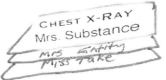

When an old-fashioned doctor is presented with a can
of worms ......

.....he automatically thinks about the Medical Defence
Organisations.....

So what did the man from the MDU say to me when
asked about clinical standards?*

*'Big cases have increased threefold over the last decade
One case settled at over a million pounds in 1995
4 cases over a million 2005
12 cases over a million in 2015
Highest was £9.2 million
Tetraplegic case,
most of the money went to the lawyers...'*

---

*(personal communication).

He continued:

'I don't have evidence that overall standards are dropping.'

'Then why the increase in large litigation cases and doctors being struck off?' I asked.

'Several possibilies including Heightened expectation, Societal approach, No win no fee lawyers and Increased complexity.'

We'll examine these factors over the next few pages in our imaginary National Elf Service.

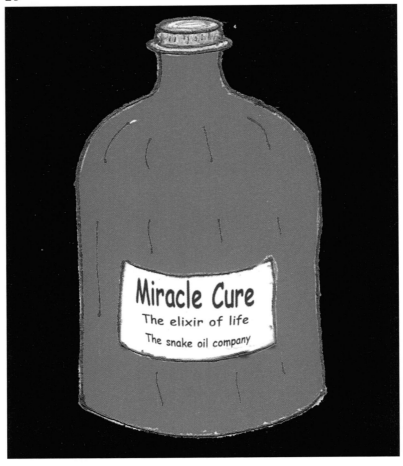

Heightened expectation

Every day the papers claim a cure for cancer or a new stem cell treatment to reverse the ageing processes. And every day the patients are disappointed when the GP cannot deliver such miracles.

Societal Approach

Some people are not grateful for (or mindful of) the work of the Elf Service:

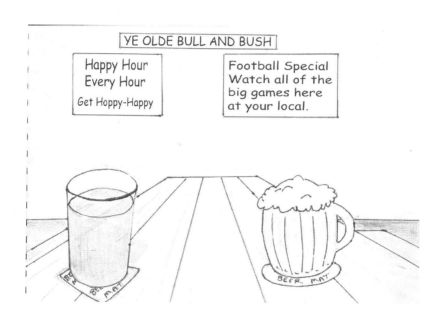

Wayne:

Hi Dave. How's Mrs Peabody?

Dave:

Okay Wayne
But she's got to have an MRI scan of her back.

Wayne:

Poor Mrs. Peabody. Bet there's a long waiting list

Dave:

Stupid beggers wanted her to go for it on Saturday.

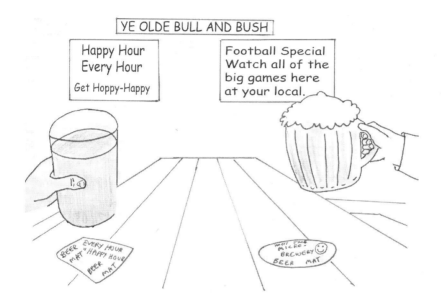

Wayne:

That's quick!

Dave:

Yeah, but she's not going. It's the FA cup!!

Wayne:

Didn't know she was a football fan like you, Dave?

Dave:

She's not but I'm not taking her down to the hospital.

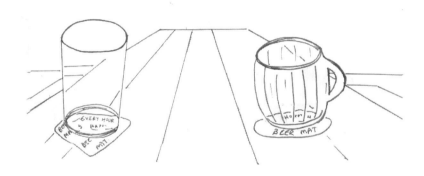

Wayne:

So she's going to miss it?

Dave:

They'll send her
another appointment.

Wayne:

Let's hope it is more convenient

Dave:

Yeah. She wants it to be on a weekday so she can have a day off work

NOTE: Last year (2015) around 5.6 million (9% of the total) NHS outpatient appointments were missed in England at an average cost of £100 per appointment.

(https://www.onmedica.com/NewsArticle.aspx?id=9aba7640-bbb2-4e15-a5a5-16452b03495b)

We have looked at:

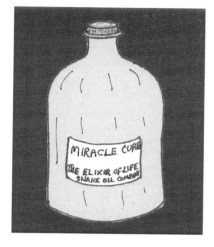

Heightened expectation,

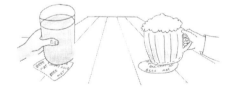

Societal approach,

And now we examine "No win no fee lawyers".
We shall look at the case of Mr. Molesworth and his broken arm.....

He arrives three minutes late at the surgery and is told by the receptionist that he has to ring the doctor who will then ring him back:

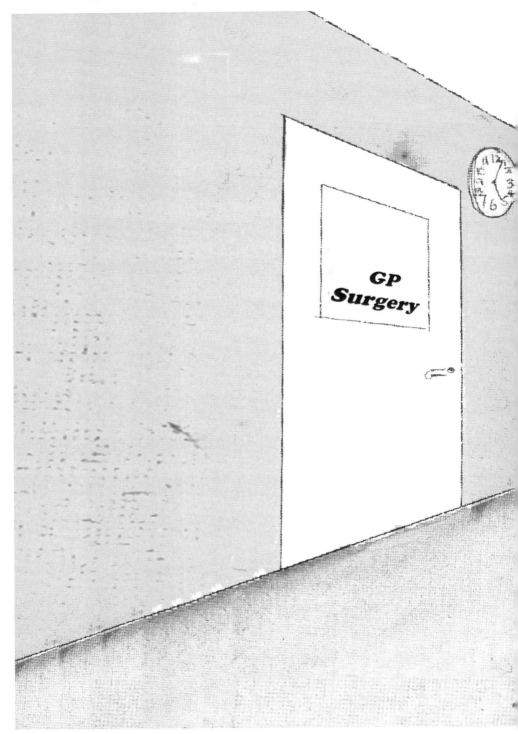

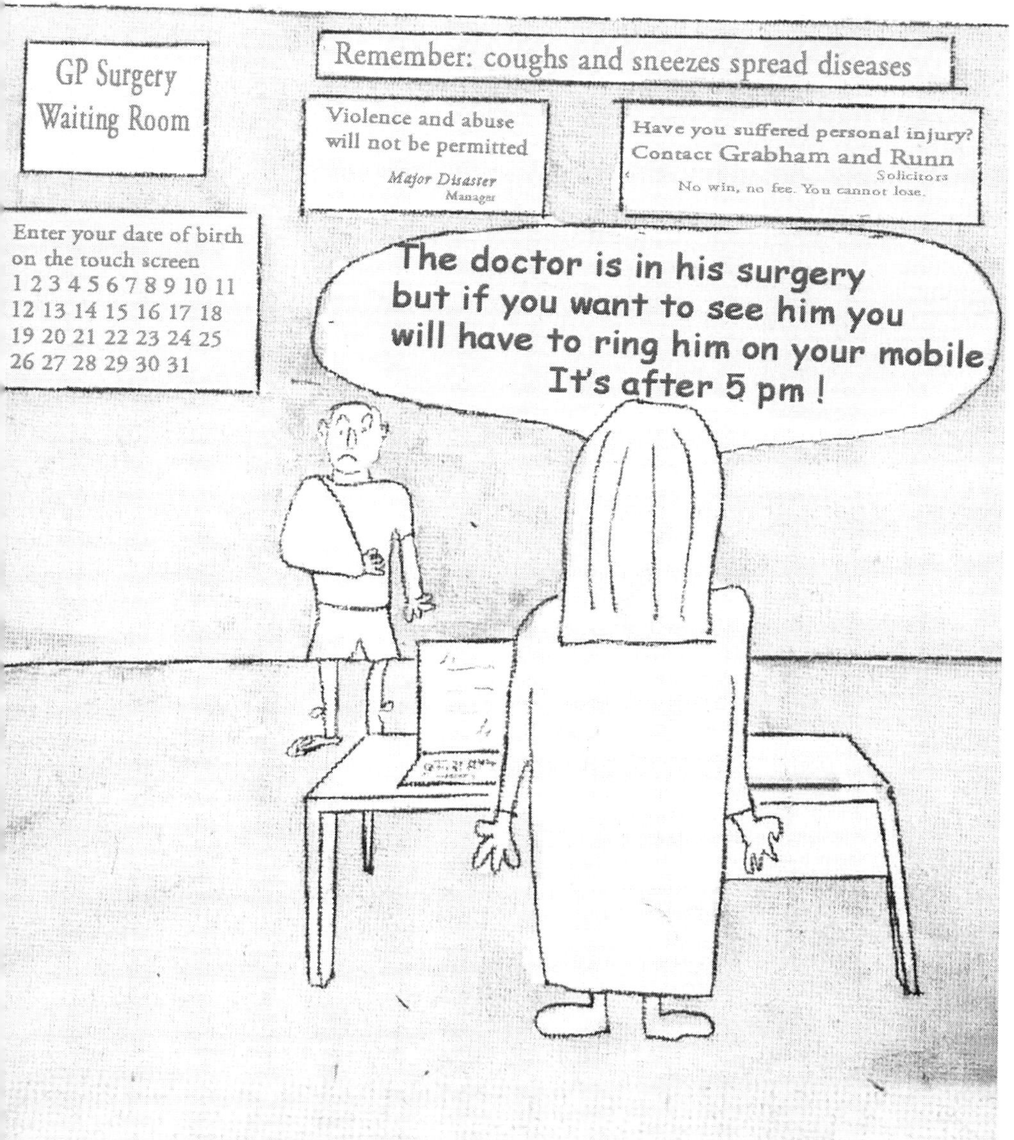
GP Surgery
Waiting Room
Remember: coughs and sneezes spread diseases
Violence and abuse
will not be permitted
Major Disaster
Manager
Have you suffered personal injury?
Contact Grabham and Runn
Solicitors
No win, no fee. You cannot lose.
Enter your date of birth
on the touch screen
1 2 3 4 5 6 7 8 9 10 11
12 13 14 15 16 17 18
19 20 21 22 23 24 25
26 27 28 29 30 31
The doctor is in his surgery
but if you want to see him you
will have to ring him on your mobile
It's after 5 pm !

He goes in to see the doctor.......and the doctor has seen him many times before and there was nothing wrong with him on any of those occasions. The doctor knows that Mr. Molesworth, like many pixies, is a confirmed hypochondriac.

Mr Molesworth replies: "I've broken my arm. I need an X-ray or a scan..."

But this doctor is trying to do his best for the Elf Service
and save it money.
It would help if he were to examine Mr. Molesworth...
but he doesn't.....

Unfortunately on this occasion Mr. Molesworth was
right. He did need an X-ray. A stethoscope is not much
help with a broken arm and the doctor did not use it...
he just waved it about like a flag.
Then he sent Mr. Molesworth off to a homeopath...

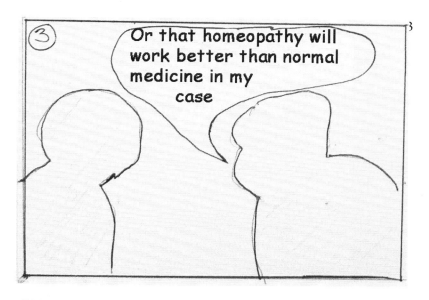

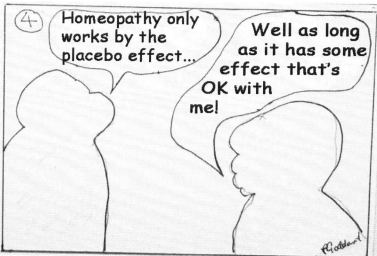

As far as I am aware homeopathic practitioners do not claim to mend broken arms and Mr. Molesworth was very dissatisfied.

He remembered the advertisement in the GP surgery....

Have you suffered personal injury?
Contact Grabham and Runn
Solicitors
No win, no fee. You cannot lose.

And he went round to their offices. There was a very reassuring brass plaque outside so he went in.

He wasn't quite so happy when he met Mr. Grabham.

And here we have Mr. Molesworth on his new toy...a mobility scooter he bought with the money from his compensation claim. He looks relatively happy although he still has a bad arm and he has put on weight.

Not as happy as Mr. Grabham who has just bought himself a classic Rolls Royce.

No, that's not Mr. Grabham driving. That's his chauffeur. Mr. Grabham is all tanked up in the back but we can't see him due to the darkened windows.

These stories were simply made up. They are all about the National Elf Service.
I'm sure nothing at all like this happens in real life.
We must now address the problem of complexity.

Heightened expectation,   **Societal approach,**

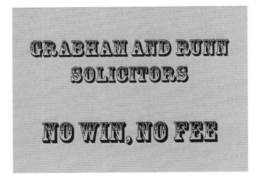

No win no fee lawyers

And Complexity.... This could be any of the following:
- Increasing complexity of the job,
- Increasing complexity of medical science
- Increasing complexity of each case

Complexity of the job is typified here by a doctor being called to three different places at the same time. It was difficult enough being on call for a couple of wards but nowadays with cross-cover and bed-saving the patients could be anywhere in the hospital. Add to that the cardiac arrest pager and calls from the Radiology Department, from Accident and Emergency and from Intensive Care and even the most competent person goes beyond their level of competence.

Simply put nobody can be in two places at the same time! (Let alone three or four!)

It still surprises some people that a Junior Doctor can be any age up to retirement. I knew a trainee radiologist who started his specialist training when he was sixty!

But amongst doctors of my age it is the young age of so many consultants that amazes us. This is due to the shortening of the time spent in specialist training and super-specialisation.

Super-specialisation has become necessary because of the major advances in medical science that have occurred over the past couple of decades.

These advances have led to increasing life expectancy and concommitant with that is increasing complexity of the patients.

Multiple Drug Use: Scotland

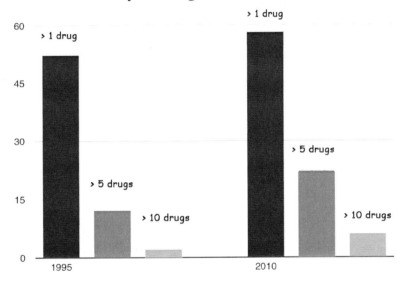

The graph above was extracted from a paper by Duerden et al from the King's Fund, entitled "Polypharmacy and medicines optimisation". The black bar is the percentage of patients on more than one drug, the mid-gray on greater than five drugs and light gray greater than ten drugs in the years 1995 and 2010. The number on more than five drugs has almost doubled whilst those on greater than ten has trebled.

When you consider that a commonly used drug such as Losartan can interact with at least 200 other drugs the complexity is mind-boggling.

The same paper points out that over the age of sixty greater than seventy percent of people in the UK have at least one chronic condition and many have several chronic ailments.

So this is a serious bit and maybe the doctors really are losing the art of medicine in the face of such complexity. What does the GMC have to say about it?

The GMC said that in total, 669 doctors have been either struck off or suspended over the last five years. Of those, only 249 were British (37 percent) while 420 (63 percent) were trained abroad—whereas one-third of doctors on the register were trained abroad, and two-thirds in Britain.

If the exponential rise in doctors being struck off doesn't get rid of us first!

European doctors were three times more likely to be struck off: GMC (Daily Telegraph Oct 2014).
And the number of complaints received by the GMC has roughly trebled over the last 15 years, from 1503 in 1995 to 4722 in 2009.

Citation: CHAMBERLAIN, J.M., 2011. The hearing of fitness to practice cases by the General Medical Council: current trends and future research agendas. Health, Risk and Society, 13 (6), pp.561-575

My mind strayed back to the National Elf Service.....had I ever left it?

Elves have changed over the years. They used to be slim and elfin (of course!)

But now they are addicted to fairy cakes the elves have become fat and lazy. (More about fairy cakes later in the book)

The same elf after eating too many cakes

The patients in the Elf Service are not always treated as well as in the NHS...sometimes they are cranked in on a giant conveyor belt..so different from our own wonderful system.

In the National Elf Service even as one patient is leaving another patient is delivered giving the poor doctor, junior or senior, no time to reflect on the last case.

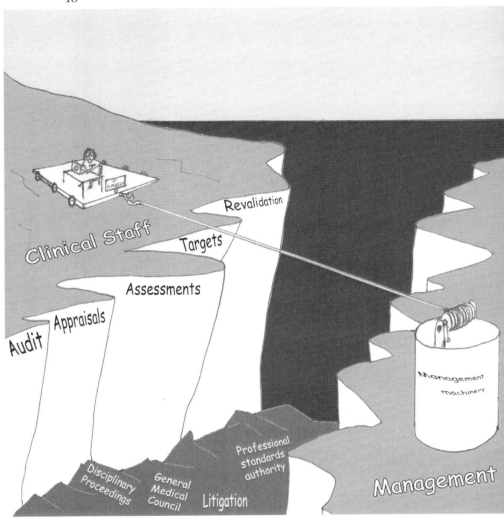

There is a huge gulf between the clinical staff and the management.

But spare a thought for the management as they are, in turn, working on a giant treadmill, forced on by some political appointee.

Who is, unfortunately, being controlled by the fat cats.
I'm so glad our NHS is not like that.

But who is in charge of the Governmental Department of National Elf in the Faerie Kingdom and in Elfdom?

I'm not hunting for compliments but I think this is quite a good likeness, don't you?
You guessed correctly. It's The Right Horrible Jellybean Shunt MP.

Oh dear! He is having a dispute with the junior doctors.

He thinks that they are dwarves working in a coal mine. Is he deluded into imagining that he is Maggie Thatcher fighting the battles of the '80's?

The junior doctor (dwarf?) has a point. It does not matter how many times the man in charge repeats himself there really are only seven days in a week and the junior doctors work on all of them already.

It seems that the man in charge is very scornful of the junior doctors (dwarves?)

He thinks that he can change reality if he stands there with his eyes glistening and repeating himself often enough.

Which is strange since he is not a wizard. Unlike the doctors he has not studied medicine (surely you mean coalmining or wizardry? ed.).

PPE is not a good training for running a National Elf Service. No wonder the junior doctor is so puzzled.

The Losing Art of Clinical Medicine

Maybe I was in danger of losing the point of the book... **The Losing Art of Clinical Medicine and how can we restore it?** So I have repeated it here.

What have we learnt?

The MDU thinks that clinical standards overall are not slipping. Maybe they base that supposition on the fact that hard indicators, such as life expectancy and infant mortality, show improvement year-on-year?

How can we square this with the fact that the GMC are erasing so many more doctors from the medical register?

Perhaps the increasingly successful science of medicine leads to a greater overall success rate but some individual medics cannot keep up with the increased complexity and the demands on their services? The loss of clinical skills in a small minority would then be masked by the undoubted achievements of the majority in executing those scientific advances.

And maybe the MDU is right and the public are simply becoming more litigious.

If we assume that the art of medicine is being lost do we know why?
The answer must be multifactorial.

The doctors may be asking for many more investigations because of loss of confidence in simple history and examination.

The many alternative ways of making the diagnosis using a variety of tests do mean that the doctor who does not order multiple investigations is more likely to be sued than one who does. If you rely on your judgement and clinical skills you are more likely to be damned than someone who investigates everybody who moves (and most of those who don't move!). Thus Shark Alert!

Patients are sometimes very knowledgeable causing a loss of confidence in the medics. This means that some doctors will spend a lot of time searching on the internet in case they have missed something when they would have been far better off talking to the patients and examining them.

Lack of time

.....And one thing of which the doctors (plus the dwarves and elves) are very short, is time.

Here are some reasons for the shortage of time and some results of this chronal paucity:

- Managers demand fast throughput and there is less time for clerking and examining patients.
- Managers and politicians insist on onerous form filling for each patient...this is usually done on the ubiquitous computer.
- Unfortunately the computers at different locations frequently do not successfuly communicate with each other due to the failure of the electronic computer record. (A scandalous failure that cost the

National Elf Service billions of pounds.) So the form filling has to be repeated ad infinitum.

- There are increasing numbers of patients (for example the total number of Accident and Emergency attendances went up by 25% between 2004 and 2014. Admissions from A and E over the same period increased by 33%!)
- Decreased number of hours for training and working
- The senior clinicians are given little time for teaching and research in their new contracts.
- Decreased time is scheduled for seeing each patient
- And there is a shortage of doctors.

Just to be perverse I will take this last point first. This is a cartoon book not a textbook so I can do that if I want to!

So why *is* there a shortage of doctors in the UK?

More doctors than ever before have been trained but still there are not enough for the workload.

There are several reasons for this:

- As mentioned earlier the workload and the complexity have both increased
- All doctors work fewer hours than comparable doctors twenty or thirty years ago (partly due to the working time directive).
- Many are now working part-time
- Many of the doctors trained in the UK have left the country: for example a third of NHS Accident & Emergency doctors have fled abroad in the past five years, due to "toxic" levels of pressure (Daily Telegraph 22 Sep 2015).

Similar problems have beset the National Elf Service....

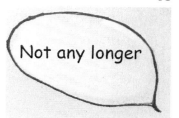

More hunting for the political problems later but now to consider, for a while, the effects of management....

Management Effects in the National Elf Service

I have argued elsewhere* that business-style management in the NHS has never been effective because the NHS cannot be run as a business .... a free service paid from taxation is the opposite to a free-market business.

* The History of Medicine, Money and Politics, P R Goddard, 2008, Clinical Press

And very effective it was as long as the clinical staff were allowed to run it. It also ran at considerably less expense than other health services that were insurance-based or compared with the private sector in the UK.

But unfortunately management have got their hands on the National Elf Service to the detriment of all (except themselves!)

How did that happen and what has been the effect?

In the National Elf Service the hospitals (coal mines?) used to be run by two people plus the assistance of all the clinical staff. The two administrators were the Matron and the Medical Superintendent. The latter was a doctor, somewhat pitied by the other consultants.

And of course the matron was the most senior nurse.

Matron

The Matron was the most feared figure in the hospital. Respected and obeyed even by the most senior doctors the matron kept all the staff on their toes. Working directly under her were the senior nurses (ward sisters, accident and emergency sisters, theatre sisters, night sisters). They kept the wards spick and span, the operating theatres clean and efficiently run, not allowing a speck of dust or filth to appear, insisting that all the pixies and elves in their hospital beds were washed and polished and that everything ran like clockwork.

Then came the Salmon report and the sisters were demoted in the hierarchy, nursing officers appeared in the corridors to tell them what to do. "Lay" sector administrators were appointed to run the hospitals.. they had no medical or nursing training.

Under Thatcher (in Elfdom?) managers were appointed and the top dog became the Chief Executive Officer with a tier of managers reporting to him or her.

Managers in the National Elf Service exist to serve themselves, maintain their own position and aim for advancement. They do this by creating problems and setting more junior managers the task of solving those artificial conundra. This is called the art of delegation. Naturally, as they have no clinical training, they cannot do any of the actual work but they can set tasks for the clinical staff to do. The fact that the clinical staff are already overworked does not worry the managers as long as they can bully the more junior staff into submission. The staff they cannot overcome in that way will be disciplined, suspended and finally sacked...often citing imaginary infractions of non-existing policies and directives whilst the managers blithely break their own rules.....

Thank goodness that is what happens in the National Elf Service and not the NHS!

What has the Chief Executive Officer, the top manager in the hospital, secreted away in her briefcase?

A whole series of hidden agendas....

So let us look at some of the silly decisions that managers in the National Elf Service have made.

(Not necessarily the silliest, just common examples)....

TEA

It is generally acknowledged in Elfdom that a cup of tea keeps people alert, working hard and gives them a boost thus improving their efficiency and output.
Oh good...here comes the tea lady....

No, I'm sorry. The managers have decided that the tea lady is no longer needed.

So the consultant is asking Smithers, the junior dwarf, to make the tea. They are on the ward round and when they have finished they will all sit down with the sister and maybe a staff nurse or two and discuss, very productively, the patients on the ward.

Notice how smart the consultant is. Can you see the consultant's name above each bed and the patient's details at the end of the bed?

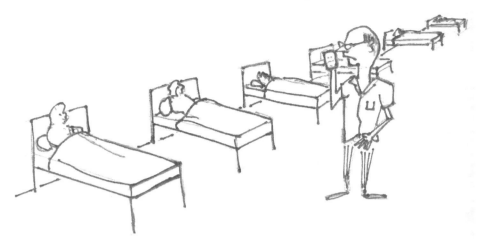

Oh dear. None of that is happening any more.

The consultant is trying to do his ward round but because of cross cover the junior dwarf is on a completely different ward. The sister is busy 'doing reports' on the computer. The consultant's name is not above the bed and, due to patient confidentiality, there are no details about the patient at the foot of the bed. So the consultant has no idea which patients he should be seeing.

Not only that he also looks a complete mess. He is not allowed to wear his jacket or tie and has to wear a short sleeved shirt and no watch. This is to prevent cross-infection (despite never proving that tie and shirt were a problem).

His name badge no longer has his title on it so he threw it away. A pity really since he needed it to get through the myriads of security doors. No wonder he looks so frazzled! And he can't even get anything to eat....

The chief executive who ordered all these changes was finally ousted when her activities were shown to be counter-productive and that she was fiddling the financial books.

But you can see that she is a well-balanced individual with a chip on each shoulder.

Don't feel at all sorry for her. She left with a big "golden handshake" and was immediately taken on as the chief executive at the neighbouring trust. They were so much in the red that they *wanted* someone who could fiddle the books. In fact they have given her a pay rise!

The consultant works at both the trusts and he had hoped that he had seen the last of her. But no, here she is turning up like a bad penny!

Oh dear. She is now making the junior dwarves work more than 48 hours a week so that they can "complete their training". This is against the rules in Faerie just as it is in the UK but she has bullied them into putting only 48 hours on their forms so that they appear compliant! No wonder the doctors don't trust her!

Young Smithers has been promoted and is working in another Trust. He has become a consultant and has been trying to set up a large research facility. Here he is talking to the new chief executive (notice that the CEO has brought a coffee for himself but not for Dr. Smithers) ......

So the young management acolytes are up to the same tricks as their former boss. Perhaps even worse?

They've all taken their cue from their ultimate boss, The Right Horrible Jellybean Shunt...

PPE certainly seems to be enough for the man himself!

78

I think we can see on the next page why Jellybean Shunt's friend Stephen did not like the Red Dragon .... It didn't want to kiss him anywhere! Now he is out in the cold.....

Why are the nurses keeping quiet?

Unfortunately the nurses in the National Elf Service were led astray by their own leaders way back at the time of the Salmon Report.

And despite constant statements to the opposite effect many of the staff are afraid to become whistleblowers. It is true that whistleblowing is allowed in the National Elf Service but only if you whistleblow *to* your managers not if you whistleblow *about* them.

And they have been passing new laws and directives that make whistleblowing ever more hazardous

Such as ?

For example the latest UK Anti-lobbying laws and the Trade Secrets Protection Directive from the EU.

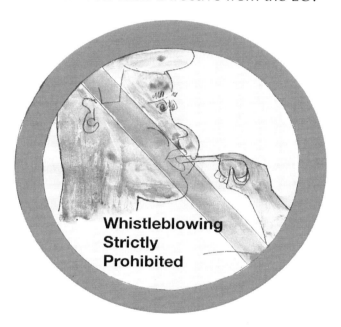

Whistleblowing Strictly Prohibited

Why did the senior doctors in the National Elf Service not speak up? Let's ask one...

The Totally Frank TV Show

All the participants are on Truth Drugs!

Interviewer	Welcome to the Totally Frank TV show in which our participants are on truth drugs. Today we interview Sir Stanley Smug, the famous surgeon.
Sir Stanley Smaug	Hello Eileen. The name is Smaug, Stanley Smaug.
Interviewer	Welcome Sir Stanley Smaug. Sir Stanley, you were President of the Royal College of Sweatshops. Why did you not protest when you saw that things were going wrong in the National Elf Service?
Sir Stanley Smaug	Good question, Eileen. May I compliment you on your appearance?
Interviewer	No Sir Stanley. Just answer the question.
Sir Stanley Smaug	I didn't say anything because I was more worried about getting my knighthood and my merit award. That's why. Did I just say that on prime time TV?
Interviewer	Yes you did. Spoken honestly on the truth drug.

Sir Stanley Smaug:	Well, it is a fact.
Interviewer:	And now that you have retired why have you still said nothing?
Sir Stanley Smaug:	Two reasons. I'm lazy and I'm greedy. I can't be bothered to fight the system and I'm too busy working at the Cash and Carry.
Interviewer:	Cash and Carry? What do you mean?
Sir Stanley Smaug:	Sorry. I mean the private goldmine, of course.
Interviewer:	Why did you call it the Cash and Carry>
Sir Stanley Smaug:	The patients have the cash and I simply carry it away.

84

It's not like that really in the NHS (are you sure? ed.).
For a start it is unusual these days for a consultant,
even a surgeon, to actually be a dragon like Sir Stanley
Smaug. The consultants in the NHS work many more
hours than they are contracted for and the senior figures
have been speaking out in support of the juniors.

Meanwhile in the National Elf Service that man "The
Right Horrible Jellybean Shunt MP" thinks he has won
a great victory......

The ambulances are queuing up outside Accident and Emergency. They cannot take their patients in until the official waiting period has dropped!

Interviewer: Welcome to our programme.

That man: Hello

Interviewer: You are looking very pleased with yourself.

That man: Yes. The juniors have gone back to work and we will achieve a 24/7 service in the coal mines.

Interviewer: Don't you mean the National Elf Service hospitals?

That man: Yes, those as well.

Interviewer: But what about the other staffing levels?

That man: No problem. They will all fall in line now.

Interviewer: But aren't they already providing the service during the weekdays?

That man: They are working during the week. But we will persuade them to work longer hours.

Interviewer: That will require extra funding.

That man: It will be achieved within the present budget.

Interviewer: That's surely impossible!

That man: It's the magic of the National Elf Service.

Interviewer: Thank you. Now we must leave our "Pie in the Sky" interview with Jellybean Shunt MP. The programme has been brought to you on the back of "Pigs That Fly" in "Cloud Cuckoo Land." Thank you and good night!

The War on Fairy Cakes

I mentioned earlier in the book that the elves had become addicted to fairy cakes. The Prime Minister in Elfdom, Darcy Macaroon, decided, in his wisdom, to copy a policy enacted in the real world. He declared war on fairy cakes. He took as his model the so-called War on Drugs..... And the results were very similar.
Cakes are not a true addiction in the real world...they are just a bad habit. In Faerie they are as addictive as Heroin. After the War on Fairy Cakes had been declared the only legal substitute, equally addictive but much nastier, was Goblin Poo (methadone?).

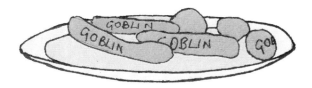

Because fairy cakes were so addictive the elves still wanted them. But they were now illegal and very expensive. Soon the addict would run out of money and start stealing, selling his or her body or, more safely as the outcome was less individually dangerous, start dealing in fairy cakes. Six addicts were needed to supply enough money for each original addict.

Each of the six would also start dealing in fairy cakes. This led to an exponential rise in the use of the cakes and a hugely fat, slothful population of addicted elves. Even the illegal cake manufacturers are worried as the consumption is outpacing supply.

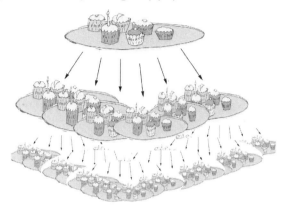

Any situation where the original participant needs to create more copies of themselves in order to survive can lead to such a Malthusian dilemma.

The elves have a similar problem in their National Elf Service. The management seem to rely on getting other people to do the work they should do themselves. This is known as delegation (see page 64). To demonstrate that they are worthy of advancement in rank and pay the managers must show the line management above them that they are capable of commanding the managers below them. They need to create more managers in inferior ranks to do this. They, in turn, create more managers to do the work their manager has delegated to them. Why does the song "I'm busy doing nothing" come to mind?

What happened to Mrs Peabody?

I'm a retired doctor and my wife is a retired dentist. We have helped to resuscitate people and deal with medical emergencies on aeroplanes, trains, buses, at a funeral, in the roads, at a retirement party, outside Accident and Emergency, in the surgery, in the hospital corridor etcetera, etcetera.

My obstetric training was of considerable significance when I assisted at emergencies during the births of both my sons and once on the Isle of Skye when I was called on to help deliver a lamb!

Poor old Smithers. The stress in the National Elf Service has done him in. But don't get too upset. He is a fictional Elf doctor and, like a cat or a sphinx, he has nine lives.

My friends in the NHS who sadly died too young were not so lucky.

Finally out of the can of worms....

Like Pandora's box there must surely be a little hope for
the Faerie Folk working in the National Elf Service...

So What Can Be Done?

I promised earlier in this book to make a few suggestions as to how the National Elf Service could be improved and saved from its own and its leaders' follies.
Here are a few ideas:

- We need more doctors: train more in UK
- Allow the senior doctors more time for teaching
- Improve the language skills of doctors from overseas.
- Renegotiate the PFI contracts. They were never fair in the first place.
- Persuade managers that they must lead by example, especially over pay.

And now the three most important ideas:

- **Education of the public: they must be taught that rights come with responsibilities.**

- **Encouragement to whistleblowers**

- **Equivalent to General Medical Council for managers. The setting of a regulating body over managers in the health sector and in education.**

Our National Elf Service manager is trying hard to be a good person. This is not an easy task for someone trained in the bullying and lying ways of the management of the National Elf Service but now that they have set up a **General Management Council** with a **National Register of Managers** she is afraid to step out of line.

Above her hangs the sword of Damocles that all doctors have feared for the past century and a half.

Just before he left office Darcy Macaroon, the former Elf PM, agreed to the creation of a management professional register. Now, like all other health care workers, they are controlled and can be struck off if necessary.

Unfortunately this change has only come into existence in the fictional world of the National Elf Service.

Maybe one day we shall see something similar in the NHS?

We live in hope...